MARTIN AND JUDY
IN THEIR TWO LITTLE HOUSES

MARTIN AND JUDY

IN THEIR TWO LITTLE HOUSES

by VERNA HILLS

VOLUME ONE

ILLUSTRATIONS BY
Charlotte Ware

CHAPTER HEAD DRAWINGS BY
W. KING INGERSOLL

THE BEACON PRESS, BOSTON, MASS.
1948

A WORD TO PARENTS AND TEACHERS

THESE stories of Martin and Judy have been written for three- and four-year-old children to be used both by teachers in nursery schools and by parents in homes. It has been found, however, that five- and six-year-olds enjoy the stories equally well. Indeed, the older children, having had more experiences themselves of the kinds described, and being more ready to question and to think aloud, may live with the stories in their imaginative play longer than the younger children and consequently may enjoy them more fully.

Since as adults we grow accustomed to viewing the things of everyday as commonplace, we are now and again startled to witness children's excited wonder in the presence of things that to us seem uninterestingly ordinary; such for example, as a small bug crawling out of a crack in the pavement, or a moving shadow cast against a wall, or a muddy pool reflecting the clouds in the sky. To three- and four-year-old children, however, life is so fresh and new that any day is likely to bring to them the thrill of a first discovery.

At such moments, small children may not be vocal. Yet an understanding parent will sense the meaning of a quivering, jumping body, or of a strangely quiet figure standing with gleaming eyes staring long at some particular spot. Other three- and four-year-olds will be able to use the crude language tools which they have acquired, and they will ask their *whys*, and *what fors*, and *hows*, seeking to reach somehow back of the apparent mystery which they confront.

Even though these young children may not be able to speak their thoughts, even though they may not really think at all, the deep or lively emotions they feel at such moments cannot but affect the learnings finally worked out as other experiences of similar types are added as the days pass by. Surely, this power of the little child to thrill with wonder at the everyday things about him is too precious to be discouraged, and too significant in its possibilities, for either the expansion or the dwarfing of the spirit, to be neglected.

Gilbert K. Chesterton in his book, *The Colored Lands*, says that all of us should "cultivate the power of seeing plain things in a kind of sunlight of surprise." He calls this art "the beginning of the praise of God." If for no other reason than for the sake of maintaining our intimacy with young children, we should revive this art of wonder, for to a courageous, unspoiled, and reasonably intelligent little child, it is as natural as eating, and vital to both his mental and his spiritual health. May it not be also for the child, as well as for the adult, that this art of wonder is, as Mr. Chesterton calls it, "the beginning of the praise of God"? Putting its significance in another way, we may say that in such experiences of surprise and wonder, there is a precious something like a germ cell from which spiritual insights may grow.

It is from a point of view linked with the emphasis given by Mr. Chesterton that these stories of Martin and Judy have been planned and written. After analyzing many of the natural experiences of three- and four-year-old children, we have chosen certain types which seem to us to have in them this core of special significance. We should not designate them as religious experiences in the usual meaning of the term. We do think of them, however, as representative experiences holding within their framework a possible element from which religious experiences may grow. These first experiences can be had by children too young to understand any theological terms. In fact, theological terminology during these early years may prove a hindrance rather than a means to spiritual development.

The types of experience which we have chosen to put into these narratives are the following:

1. We have chosen experiences which bring little children into contact with the great forces of nature, such as rain, snow, sunshine, and winds. We believe that when facing these forces, little children should begin to discover that in these natural happenings there is to be found an orderliness of sequence and a degree of dependability that we sense more clearly the more we understand nature's so-called laws. Through such direct experiences with nature, children should gradually come to realize that there are large and enveloping powers which are beyond the ken and the control of human beings; in short, that humanity shares a common dependence upon an inconceivably great unifying power that somehow seems to have planned and seems to control the universe.

In dealing with the natural forces as children experience them, we have purposely avoided any use of the word or thought of a personal God, for if children reach this great Creative Power too easily and too quickly, they will inevitably picture a man-god who acts from personal motives either of anger or of love. An untrue conception of the causes of rain and droughts, floods and tornadoes may then result, producing resentment on the child's part, or a feeling of favoritism or of unfairness, and a possible personal dislike for God. The Creator God is too great to be adequately interpreted to a four-year-old. It is probably better that a child should first have many simply guided experiences with the greatness, the orderliness, and the reasonable dependability of nature before he is led to conceive of a definite God as the ultimate Source of all.

2. A second type of experience which we have chosen is had when children are first challenged by the difference between animate and inanimate things. Children are not born already knowing what it means to live. They must experience this. They must watch the live thing alongside the non-living thing. At such a moment of awakening when the discovery is first made, a little child finds himself face to face with the ultimate mystery of life, the power within a thing to grow and to feel and perhaps to think. Such an experience is probably significant beyond our dreaming. It may prove as revelatory to the small child as any religious experience can be to an adult.

3. Related to this first experience in discovering the essential nature of a living thing, is the discovery that living things are born. It may be the sight of the birth of kittens. It may be the hatching of chicks. It may be the birth of a baby sister or brother. Again the challenge is probably tremendous. Eventually the child will apply the discovery to himself, and wonderings about his own birth will begin. Where did he come from? Where was he when Mother was a little girl? Who took care of him then? The acceptance of the fact that there was once a time when he was not—in the sense that he now is—may bring to a child his first awareness of his separateness from his parents. It may cause his first painful sense of his *alone-ness*. Yet out of this very pain will grow a realization of his uniqueness and private responsibility for his own life. The religious faiths of mankind have always been linked with a recognition of the mystery in the birth of living things. It is probable that something very significant for a child's religion also depends on what he discovers when he is first aware of his own birth.

4. A fourth type of experience which we have chosen to put into narrative form is to be found when children first discover the fact of death. This almost certainly comes before the end of the fourth year. The great fascination which a dead thing has for a young child is itself testimony to the significance of this first

discovery. An unnecessarily dark shadow falls upon many young children because of the mishandling of this first experience. On the other hand, the first courageous acceptance of death as a natural part of life puts a certain stamina into the soul, and lengthens the perspective from which a child may look at the span of his lifetime. Death has again and again brought mankind to its knees. The child's first experience with this stupendous fact must also have a religious significance. In fact, most parents feel the importance of this first contact so deeply that they evade the issue in fear of making some disastrous mistake. In these volumes and in the Guide for Parents and Teachers accompanying these volumes, we have attempted to suggest ways of facing sincerely this experience with death.

5. A fifth type of story deals with early experiences with sickness. These periods often prove crucial in children's spiritual development. Sickness brings, on the one hand, the need to face pain and to learn self control under hard circumstances for the sake of future good. On the other hand, sickness sometimes causes the growth of a fear of unseen dangers, or the building up of an abnormal craving for affectionate attention, or the development of an unwholesome desire to prolong the feelings of helplessness. All these—some high values, other destructive trends—are latent as possibilities in children's early experiences with sickness. Some narratives in these volumes, it is hoped, may suggest constructive attitudes that may be developed during such crises.

6. Another type of experience put into narrative form in these volumes is children's play with shadows. Again, children's very fascination with these experiences seems to suggest their significance. Perhaps in their excited interest, children are reflecting a primitive reaction. Simple nature peoples have usually reacted to shadows with a similar mystification and have linked them with the world of spirit. Mankind has commonly believed his shadow to be one of his illusive souls. Whatever may be the true explanation of children's interest in their shadows, they should be led through such experiences away from superstitious fears into an understanding enjoyment.

7. A seventh type of experience contained in these stories is that which brings to children the need to clarify their understanding of the world of reality (as we call it) as distinguished from the world of dreams and fancies, without leading to the false conclusion that one world is more important than the other.

In such stories as the two on Martin's dreams, we have suggested the amazing nature of the power to dream. In this recognition somehow lies the discovery that the mind is able in part to transcend the limitations of the body. It must be a moment of awakening for a little child when he is first aware that his thoughts can travel unseen, and that they can reach far beyond the boundaries marked by the functioning of his feet or his ears or his eyes. To many children, however, their nighttime dreams suggest merely silly or fearful happenings, and their daytime flights of fancy call forth only condemnation from their elders; while certain Bible stories commonly told to small children suggest the thought, to some children appalling, that God sometimes speaks in dreams.

There is surely need for a more intelligent handling of these experiences. We see rich possibilities in developing a free and intelligent attitude toward dreaming. There is something thrilling in the thought that our greatest powers are invisible —our powers to think, to imagine, and to feel. How can a child really catch the significance of the invisibility of God until he has first realized the invisibility of his own real psyche?

8. We have chosen a number of stories also in which are portrayed experiences in social co-operation, sometimes within the family circle, and sometimes with the larger community beyond the home. The recognition that each one of us is but one member in a larger social body and that different members have differing functions may be called a religious discovery. It is again a germinal experience without which a larger appreciation of the brotherhood of all mankind can never grow. There are many stories in these two volumes that reveal Martin and Judy as learning to respect the views of others, or as sharing in the responsibilities in the home, or even as making their sacrifices for the good of the larger group. Throughout the stories one feels the warmth of the sense of belonging to a home circle—a feeling which forms the rootage without which vital social feelings for those outside the home circle tend to wither. We hope that these stories may encourage, for the children who read them, happier experiences of their own of this general nature. Then later when ideals of kindliness and love and mutual respect are put into language form, these children will be able to respond with the feeling that they have already learned these things by themselves in their own experiences.

9. Although experiences of a negative sort have, for the most part, been omitted from these volumes, yet they are not entirely absent, as will be noted in the story called "Teasing." Once in a while the attitudes of mutual respect and love which link people together can be seen more clearly if found in contrast to the attitudes of jealousy and disrespect which separate people. Children even in the nursery may be helped to see for themselves the results of their experiments in social living—noting the consequences of different types of action and attitude. A shallow outward conformity is likely to follow when children are taught largely by precept the so-called Christian virtues. Only when they have an opportunity to learn direct for themselves, through observing the results that follow their different modes of conduct, will they begin to realize that the law of cause and effect prevails not only in the realm of physical phenomena, but that also in the realm of human relationships we reap what we sow.

10. There are stories also portraying personal creative achievements of a concrete sort, growing out of original planning and purposing. The Christmas stories contain this element. These original creations are so deeply enjoyed by children that one can scarcely help but recognize something godlike in the experience.

These spiritual values are enhanced if under such circumstances children are not praised in ways that lead to the centering of their thoughts merely upon themselves, but if their contributions are appreciated because of certain qualities in them, and because of their worth to the group with whom they are shared. Such experiences can never be given children through instruction. Parents and teachers may only grant children the opportunities to have them.

11. We have chosen also to present our story children as making choices when they have need to weigh a present good over against a future one. The stories of Martin and his money are especially rich in this regard. Such experiences help children to mature in their ability to make ethical discriminations, and in their ability to control their actions purposefully. These learnings are fundamental if the higher spiritual qualities of character are to be achieved.

12. Finally, we have chosen to write several stories in which we present Martin and Judy as taking by themselves certain steps in order to overcome difficulties, and as having in consequence a consciousness of growth in inner strength. Such

experiences are described in the stories entitled "The Great Big Dog" and "Night-time." Many adults find in times of prayer this lift of the spirit that comes with a feeling of growth. For small children, it is probably gained more naturally in just such experiences as Miss Hills has described. We should not blind ourselves to the reality of the high values in the experiences simply because they were not gained when kneeling in prayer. These children may come later to realize that at such moments of inner strength, they have actually drawn upon resources far greater than those within their own small egos. Let us first, however, so guide children that they may, at least, have such experiences.

The choice of episodes used in these two series of stories, then, has been made on the basis of a philosophy that a natural spiritual development is possible and desirable for little children. We have purposely avoided the telling of Bible stories because, in our judgment, little children are not ready for them. Three- and four-year-olds have too meagre a conception of the passing of time to be ready for stories of the past. Their personalities will grow more naturally if they are helped to understand and to appreciate the values in their own everyday living.

The stories represent, for the most part, satisfying experiences—some having in them the thrill of discovery. Those narrated have been chosen with the purpose to accent, for children and for parents and teachers reading to children, certain significant experiences which have been too often omitted from story books. They are experiences which have in them fundamental elements belonging to worthy religious experiences.

All references to God, however, have been intentionally omitted. Our philosophy is that unverbalized experiences should come before religious language is used for describing them. The vocabularies of three- and four-year-old children are meagre and their words for the most part represent concrete things and actions. We find that words, given to little children before they have had the experiences needed to clothe those words with meanings, are liable to dwarf growth rather than to stimulate it. Misunderstandings arise and thoughts are fixed on a childish level. Curiosities instead of being aroused for further exploration, may become satisfied with a word, because Mother has said the word. The child's original interest is removed from the real mystery and becomes centered on the mystery in the word, and a false feeling of having plumbed the ultimate may sterilize thought. A minimum of religious vocabulary is probably preferable to a premature answering of children's wonderings with adult expressions of faith.

These books, then, can be used by parents of all faiths or by parents who cannot accept any historical form of faith at all. The stories are meant to encourage in small children a sensitivity to intangible spiritual values that are basic in all worthy religions, and in all real living that deserves to be characterized as spiritual in quality.

Through the reading of these stories either by teachers to groups of children or by parents to a single child, it is hoped that similar experiences which the real children have had may be recalled, and that other experiences of a like nature will be sought, without the parent or teacher suggesting these results. Many child listeners, if given the opportunity, will in their imaginations play Martin and Judy and re-enact many of these stories.

Let us not, however, minimize in our own minds, the values in these experiences merely because we do not talk about them, or do not use them as opportunities to give religious instruction. There is a subtle wisdom involved in knowing just how much to say to little children and how much to leave unsaid. As we seek this wisdom, let us keep before us these objectives—to preserve and develop at all times the attitude of inquiry, and the power "to see plain things in a kind of sunlight of surprise."

The Guide for Parents and Teachers by Elizabeth M. Manwell which accompanies these volumes greatly enlarges upon the positions set forth in this introduction. It also contains a few more stories for special occasions—such as times of sickness and death, and times when children ask about God—together with other concrete suggestions regarding possible procedures and why they are to be desired.

Since these books represent a new venture in the spiritual education of small children, we shall welcome criticisms and suggestions from those who may use the books with children.

SOPHIA L. FAHS,
Editor.

CONTENTS

VOLUME I

MARTIN AND JUDY
IN THEIR TWO LITTLE HOUSES

TWO LITTLE HOUSES

ONCE there were two little houses side by side. One little house was just as tall as the other little house. It was just as wide as the other little house. It was just as long as the other little house.

The two little houses had the same kind of porches. They had the same kind of chimneys. They had the same kind of windows. They had the same kind of doors. They had the same kind of yards.

The two little houses had the same kind of rooms. They had rooms to sleep in. They had rooms to eat in. They had kitchens. They had bathrooms. They had living-rooms. They had play-rooms.

The two little houses were both painted white.

When the sun was shining, it shone on both the little white houses.

When the wind was blowing, it blew on both the little white houses.

When the rain was raining, it rained on both the little white houses.

The little white houses were exactly alike. But the people who lived in the little white houses were not exactly alike.

Martin lived in one little white house. Martin's father and Martin's mother and Martin's big sister all lived there, too. So did Stubby, the dog.

Judy lived in the other little white house. Judy's father and Judy's mother and Judy's big brother all lived there, too. So did Judy's baby sister. So did Dusky, the cat.

Martin was a boy.

Judy was a girl.

Martin and Judy were friends.

Martin and Judy liked their little white houses. They liked their yards to play in.

They liked each other.

GOOD MORNING TO MARTIN AND JUDY

WAKE-up time! Wake-up time!
   Martin and Judy
      One by one
         Opened their eyes
            When night was done.

The daylight came to Martin's house. It came to Judy's house. It came to all the other houses in the town. It came to all the other towns and cities.

A bright light made a straight path across Martin's floor. It made a straight path across Judy's floor. It made straight paths across other people's floors.

Then Martin and Judy were ready to get up. They had many things to do in the two little white houses.

In one little white house, Martin cleaned his teeth.

He washed his face and hands.

He hopped into his clothes.

He brushed his hair.

He ate his breakfast.

In the other little white house, Judy cleaned her teeth.

She washed her face and hands.

She hopped into her clothes.

She brushed her hair.

She ate her breakfast.

After Martin and Judy had done all these things, they were ready to help with the housework.

   Martin and Judy
      One by one
         Worked away
            Till their work was done.

In one little white house, Martin wiped all the breakfast forks and spoons.

He hung his pajamas up in his closet.

He fed Stubby, the dog, his breakfast.

In the other little white house, Judy put all the breakfast napkins in the kitchen cupboard drawer.

She hung her pajamas up in her closet.

She fed Dusky, the cat, her breakfast.

After Martin and Judy had done all these things, they were ready to play.

Martin and Judy
One by one
Were ready to play
When work was done.

Then Martin climbed the fence in the sunshine, to play in Judy's yard.

Step, step, step, went Martin's feet, taking him down the walk to play with Judy.

"Yoo-hoo, yoo-hoo, yoo-hoo," went Martin's voice, telling Judy that he was coming.

Step, step, step, went Judy's feet, taking her down the porch to play with Martin.

"Yoo-hoo, yoo-hoo, yoo-hoo," went Judy's voice, telling Martin that she was coming.

They ran around over the grass playing tag.

Martin and Judy liked to play together.

Playing together was much more fun than playing alone.

Martin and Judy
Two by two
Thought of the nicest
Things to do.

OFF TO THE DUCK POND

JUDY and Martin and Martin's mother were going for a walk.
They were going for a walk to the pond.
They were going to see the ducks.
Up the hill they went, step, step, step.
Down the hill they went, run, run, run.
Over the wall they went, climb, climb, climb.
"We are almost there," said Martin. "Soon we shall see the pond."
"We are almost there," said Judy. "Soon we shall hear the ducks."
"Yes," said Martin's mother. "We are almost there. We will go up the path between the trees. We will go down the path beyond the trees. Then we will look for the pond."
Judy and Martin and Martin's mother walked on and on.
They went up the path between the trees.
They went down the path beyond the trees.
They looked for the pond.
They looked for the ducks.
Judy and Martin and Martin's mother looked and looked again.
They did not see any pond at all.
They did not see any ducks.
They saw just one big puddle of mud.
"What has happened to the pond?" asked Martin.
"What has happened to the ducks?" asked Judy.
Judy and Martin and Martin's mother looked and looked again.
"I did not think," said Martin's mother, "that the pond would be so dry. We have had many days of hot sunshine. We have had no rain. That is why the pond has grown smaller and smaller."
"But where are the ducks?" asked Martin.

"They have flown away to look for another pond," said Martin's mother.

"Will they come back?" asked Judy.

"We must wait and see. We must wait until it rains."

"Do you think it will rain today?" asked Martin.

Martin's mother looked up at the sky.

She saw that it was blue and bright.

She saw no clouds at all.

"No," said Martin's mother. "I don't think it will rain today."

Judy and Martin and Martin's mother turned around to go home.

They went up the path that led to the trees.

They went down the path between the trees.

Judy and Martin were wondering where the pond had gone.

Judy and Martin were wondering where the ducks had flown.

They were wishing that it would rain.

Over the wall they went, climb, climb, climb.

"Couldn't we make it rain?" asked Judy.

"No," said Martin's mother. "We could not make it rain."

Up the hill they went, step, step, step.

"Couldn't Daddy make it rain?" asked Judy.

"No," said Martin's mother. "Daddies cannot make it rain."

"Can policemen make it rain?" asked Judy. "Can firemen make it rain?"

"No," said Martin's mother. "No person can make it rain."

Down the hill they went, run, run, run.

"Why can't we make it rain?" asked Martin.

"Because we cannot make clouds come. Because we cannot make the winds blow."

"When will it rain?" asked Judy.

"When the winds blow the clouds over our heads. When the clouds spread out over the sky. Then it will rain. But I don't know when that will be."

Judy and Martin and Martin's mother were coming near the two little white houses where they lived.

Martin's mother went into the house. Martin and Judy walked up and down the yard.

They looked up at the sky.

They wished it would rain and fill the pond full.

They wished it would rain and the ducks would come back.

Judy and Martin looked up at the sky again.

They saw it was blue and bright.

They saw no clouds at all.

Judy and Martin knew that it would not rain that day.

WISHING FOR RAIN

Martin and Judy wanted the pond to fill up again.
They wanted the ducks to swim on the pond again.
Martin and Judy wished it would rain again.
They were wishing as they walked up and down the sidewalk.
They were wishing as they looked up at the sky.
"I see a little cloud," said Martin.
"Perhaps it is going to rain," said Judy.
Martin and Judy saw a man named Mr. King. He was looking at the sky, too.
"Do you think it is going to rain, Mr. King?" asked Martin.
"I hope not," said Mr. King. "I've just painted my steps. I want them to dry before it rains."
Martin and Judy saw a woman named Mrs. Smith. She was looking at the sky, too.
"Do you think it is going to rain, Mrs. Smith?" asked Judy.
"I hope not," said Mrs. Smith. "I want to go on a picnic. I can't go if it rains."
Martin and Judy turned around.
They were still wishing as they looked up at the sky.
They saw some clouds being blown about in the sky. They saw the sun peeping out between the clouds.
Martin and Judy saw Mrs. Smith again. She was still looking up at the sky.
"There's the sun," said Mrs. Smith. "It may not rain after all."
Martin and Judy saw Mr. King again. He was still looking up at the sky.
"There's the sun," said Mr. King. "It may not rain after all."

Martin and Judy went into the little white house where Martin lived.

Martin's mother smiled at them.

"Do you think it is going to rain?" asked Martin.

"I don't know," said Martin's mother. "Do you want it to rain?"

"Yes. We want it to rain and fill the pond," said Judy.

"But Mr. King doesn't want it to rain," said Martin. "Mr. King wants the paint on his steps to dry."

"And Mrs. Smith doesn't want it to rain," said Judy. "Mrs. Smith wants to go on a picnic."

"I see," said Martin's mother. "The rain will make Judy and Martin feel glad. It will make Mr. King and Mrs. Smith feel sorry."

"I wish all the people could be glad at the same time," said Martin.

"Why can't they?" asked Judy.

"People have to take turns being glad," said Martin's mother. "We can never be quite sure when our turns will come."

Martin and Judy looked out of the window.

They looked up at the sky.

They wondered how soon it would rain.

Just then —

Spatter, spatter, spatter, came some drops against the window.

"The rain is coming now," shouted Martin. "The clouds must be over our heads."

"The clouds must be very big," said Judy.

Spatter, spatter, spatter, came more drops against the window.

"It's our turn to be glad," said Judy.

"But Mr. King will not be glad. And Mrs. Smith will miss her picnic," said Martin.

Spatter, spatter, spatter, came the drops against the window.

Splash, splash, splash, came the drops upon the grass.

Martin and Judy watched and watched.

"Do you think there will be a pond again?" said Judy.

"Do you think the ducks will fly back again?" said Martin.

"Let us go for another walk soon," said Martin's mother. "And then we can see."

FIVE LITTLE DUCKS ALL IN A ROW

MARTIN and Judy ran ahead of Martin's mother.
They knew the way to the duck pond now.
They were in a hurry to be there.
"Do you think the ducks have come back?" asked Judy.
"I don't know," said Martin. "Perhaps they have found another
pond. Perhaps they like that pond better than this one."
Up the hill went Martin and Judy, step, step, step.
At the top of the hill they looked back.
They waved their hands at Martin's mother, just starting up the
hill.
Martin's mother waved her hand at them.

Down the hill went Martin and Judy, run, run, run.
At the bottom of the hill they looked back.
They could not see Martin's mother anywhere.
"Let's wait," said Martin. "Let's wait till we see my mother."
In a few minutes Martin's mother came over the top of the hill.
She waved her hand at Martin and Judy, waiting at the foot of
the hill.
Martin and Judy waved their hands at her.

Over the wall went Martin and Judy, climb, climb, climb.
"We are almost there," said Martin.
"Soon we'll see if the ducks have come back," said Judy.
Martin and Judy looked back at Martin's mother.
They waved their hands at her.
Then they began to run again.
They ran up the path between the trees.

"Listen!" said Martin.

"I hear the ducks!" said Judy. "The ducks have come back."

Martin and Judy ran down the path beyond the trees.

They saw the pond.

They saw the ducks swimming on the pond.

"Goody, goody, goody!" sang Judy.

"The ducks have come back, the ducks have come back, the ducks have come back," sang Martin.

Then Martin and Judy saw something they had not seen before.

They saw a big duck walking down the shore of the pond.

They saw one, two, three, four, five baby ducks walking behind her.

Martin and Judy watched and watched.

They saw the mother duck go into the water.

They saw one, two, three, four, five baby ducks go into the water.

"They can swim," said Martin. "The baby ducks can swim."

"Let's go back and tell your mother," said Judy. "Your mother will be surprised."

Away ran Martin and Judy, up the path that led to the trees.

They saw Martin's mother coming. They called to her.

"Come quick! Come quick!" shouted Martin.

"Surprise! Surprise!" shouted Judy.

Martin's mother ran, too.

She ran with Martin and Judy, down the path beyond the trees.

She saw the mother duck, swimming on the pond.

She saw one, two, three, four, five baby ducks, swimming after their mother.

"How lovely! Lovely!" said Martin's mother. "What cute little baby ducks they are!"

Martin and Judy and Martin's mother watched the ducks for a long time. They fed them crumbs of bread.

They found the duck's nest in the grasses by the shore.

"The mother duck must have been sitting on the eggs, when we were here before," said Martin's mother. "She must have been there all the time, and we did not see her."

Martin and Judy went back to the pond again.

They saw the mother duck swimming toward the shore.

They heard her calling, "Quack, quack, quack."

"She is calling her baby ducks," said Martin's mother.

"They are coming, they are coming," said Judy.

"Five little ducks all in a row," said Martin.

The mother duck stepped out of the water onto the grass.

The one, two, three, four, five baby ducks stepped out after her.

Away they walked, in a long line, around the shore of the pond.

BABY SISTER AND SARAH THE DOLL

JUDY'S baby sister was not very big, but she was growing bigger. Her mother wanted to know how much bigger she had grown.

So Mother laid the baby down on the little white scales in the bathroom.

Judy watched her do it.

Judy's baby sister kicked her feet up and down. She waved her hands back and forth.

It was hard to weigh Baby Sister because she would not lie still.

"How heavy is Baby today?" asked Judy.

"She weighs just eighteen pounds," said Mother.

"Is that more than she weighed the last time?" asked Judy.

"A quarter of a pound more," answered Mother. "That's just this much more." She let Judy lift one of the little weights on the scales.

Judy's mother lifted Baby Sister off the little white scales.

She then laid her down beside the long yardstick.

Judy's baby sister kicked her feet up and down. She waved her hands back and forth.

It was hard to measure Baby Sister because she would not be still.

"How tall is Baby today?" asked Judy.

"She measures just twenty-seven inches," answered Mother.

"Is that more than she measured the last time?" asked Judy.

"Almost half an inch more," answered Mother. "That's just this much more." She showed Judy with her thumb and finger.

"Baby Sister is growing bigger and bigger," said Judy.

She ran to find Sarah, the doll. She laid Sarah, the doll, on the little white scales.

Sarah, the doll, did not kick her feet up and down. She did not wave her hands back and forth.

It was easy to weigh Sarah, the doll, because she lay very still.

"How heavy is Sarah, the doll, today?" asked Judy.

"She weighs just two pounds," said Mother.

"Is that more than she weighed the last time?" asked Judy.

"No," said Mother. "That is just the same as before."

Judy lifted Sarah, the doll, off the little white scales.

Judy knew that Sarah, the doll, had not grown any heavier.

Judy then laid her down beside the long yardstick.

Sarah, the doll, did not kick her feet up and down. She did not wave her hands back and forth.

It was easy to measure Sarah, the doll, because she lay very still.

"How tall is Sarah, the doll, today?" asked Judy.

"She measures just fourteen inches," answered Mother.

"Is that taller than she was the last time?" asked Judy.

"No," said Mother. "That is just the same as before."

Mother dressed the baby and laid her in her carriage.

Judy dressed Sarah, the doll, and laid her in her carriage.

Judy knew that Sarah, the doll, had not grown any taller.

Seven mornings and seven nights went by.

Then Mother put Judy's baby sister on the little white scales again.

Judy watched her do it.

Judy's baby sister kicked her feet up and down. She waved her hands back and forth.

"How heavy is Baby Sister today?" asked Judy.

"She weighs eighteen and a quarter pounds," answered Mother.

"Is that more than she weighed the last time?" asked Judy.

"A quarter of a pound more," said Mother.

"I know," said Judy. "This much more." She found the little weight and lifted it.

Mother took Baby Sister off the little white scales.

She said, "Are you going to weigh Sarah, the doll, today?"

"No," said Judy. "I know how much Sarah, the doll, weighs. She weighs just two pounds."

"Oh," said Mother. "Then you don't think she has grown any?"

Judy shook her head. "Sarah, the doll, doesn't really grow," she said. "We make-believe she grows. We make-believe she eats. We make-believe she sleeps."

"Oh, I see," said Mother.

"Babies really eat and sleep. They really grow. They are alive. By and by Baby will be big like me." Judy stopped to think a minute. "When Baby gets big, we can play together. That will be fine. We can play with Sarah, the doll."

So Judy's baby sister kept on growing bigger.

Judy kept on growing bigger.

Sarah, the doll, stayed just the right size for Judy and Baby to play with.

BABY SISTER DOES SOMETHING NEW

Judy and Martin were having fun with the wagon and the kiddie-kar.

They went from Judy's back yard to Judy's front porch.

On the front porch were Judy's mother and Martin's mother. They were knitting new suits.

Near the front porch was Judy's baby sister. She was crawling in her play pen.

Judy and Martin kept on having fun with the wagon and the kiddie-kar. They went from Judy's front porch to the sidewalk.

On the sidewalk was Judy's big brother. He was playing marbles with his friends.

On the lawn near the sidewalk was Martin's big sister. She was having a meeting with her friends.

Martin's big sister and her friends were busy. They did not say anything to Judy and Martin.

Judy's big brother and his friends were busy. They said, "Don't run over our marbles."

Judy and Martin kept riding along with the wagon and the kiddie-kar. They went from the sidewalk to Judy's front porch.

Judy's mother and Martin's mother were busy. They said, "Run along and have a good time."

Judy's baby sister was not busy. She was very glad to see Judy and Martin. She crawled around in her pen. She laughed and clapped her hands.

Judy and Martin stopped to speak to Judy's baby sister. They watched her crawling in her pen.

"Look, look, Martin," said Judy. "Baby is trying to stand up."

"She can't do it, can she?" said Martin. "If she tries, she will sit down hard."

"Let's ride some more," said Judy.

Away rode Judy and Martin with the wagon and the kiddie-kar. They rode from Judy's front porch to the sidewalk. They rode as far as Martin's lawn.

They turned around. They rode back again.

When they came near to Judy's front porch, Judy stopped riding.

"Look, Martin, look," said Judy. "Baby Sister is trying again. She's trying to stand up."

Martin looked at the baby in her pen.

"Your baby *is* standing up," said Martin. "A little while ago she couldn't do it, and now she can."

Judy and Martin left the wagon beside the baby's pen. They left the kiddie-kar with the wagon.

Away ran Judy and Martin, up the steps to the front porch.

"Come and see! Come and see!" shouted Judy and Martin. "The baby is standing up!"

Judy's mother and Martin's mother put down their knitting. They looked over the railing of Judy's front porch.

Away ran Judy and Martin, from the front porch to the sidewalk.

"Come and see! Come and see!" shouted Judy and Martin. "The baby is standing up."

Judy's big brother and his friends left their marbles on the sidewalk. They raced up the driveway to the baby's pen.

Martin's big sister and her friends stopped their meeting on the lawn. They ran straight to the baby's pen.

Judy's baby sister sat down in her pen. After a few minutes she stood up again. She held on to the sides of the pen. She looked very glad.

Everybody wanted to see the baby standing up.

Everybody looked and looked again.

"A little while ago the baby couldn't stand up," said Judy. "She tried and she couldn't do it. Then she tried some more and she could."

"The baby is growing up, I guess," said Martin.

"By and by she will learn to do some more things," said Judy's mother. "She will learn to do all the things that you can do."

BABY AND DOLLY GO RIDING, RIDING

JUDY'S baby sister was riding in her carriage.

Sarah, the doll, was riding beside her.

Judy's baby sister was bouncing and laughing. Sarah, the doll, was sitting still.

Judy pushed the carriage along.

Judy's mother walked close beside her.

Away went Baby Sister, riding, riding with Sarah, the doll.

Away went Judy's mother, walking, walking close beside them.

"Good afternoon, Mr. King," said Judy's mother.

"Well, well," said Mr. King, "how the baby has grown. She will soon be walking, I'm sure."

"She can stand up now," said Judy.

Away went Baby Sister, riding, riding with Sarah, the doll.

Away went Judy's mother, walking, walking close beside them.

"Good afternoon, Mrs. Smith," said Judy's mother.

"Good afternoon," said Mrs. Smith. "Can the baby walk yet?"

"No, but she can stand up," said Judy.

Away went Baby Sister, riding, riding with Sarah, the doll.

Away went Judy's mother, walking, walking close beside them.

Judy turned and pushed the carriage up into Mrs. Perkins's yard. Mrs. Perkins was weeding her flower bed.

"Our baby can stand up now," said Judy.

"Oh," said Mrs. Perkins, "I wish I could see her do it."

"I think," said Judy's mother, "Baby Sister could stand by the carriage."

So Judy's mother lifted Baby Sister down to the ground.

Baby Sister stood up holding on to the carriage.

Judy lifted Sarah, the doll, down to the ground.

Sarah, the doll, stood leaning on the carriage.

"See," said Judy. "They are both standing up."

Baby Sister looked at Sarah, the doll. She reached her arms out to pick up the doll.

"Oh, dear," said Judy's mother, when she saw what was happening.

Baby Sister and Sarah, the doll, both fell down.

They both bumped their heads on the ground.

Baby Sister began to cry.

Sarah, the doll, lay very still. She did not cry.

Judy's mother picked up the baby. She kissed Baby Sister's head.

Judy picked up the doll. She kissed the doll's head, too.

"Did your doll hurt her head?" asked Mrs. Perkins.

"No," said Judy. "Bumps don't really hurt dolls. Dolls don't really cry, either. We just make-believe they cry."

"Oh, I see," said Mrs. Perkins. "Bumps really hurt babies. So they cry."

"Yes," said Judy. "Bumps really hurt babies, just as they hurt me."

Judy's mother put Baby Sister back in the carriage.

Judy put Sarah, the doll, down beside her.

Judy's baby sister stopped crying. She began to laugh and pull at Sarah, the doll.

"Look," said Judy, "The baby is laughing now. Let's make-believe that Sarah, the doll, is laughing, too."

Judy pushed the carriage out of the yard.

Judy's mother walked close beside her.

Away went Baby Sister, riding, riding with Sarah, the doll.

Away went Judy's mother, walking, walking close beside them.

A BONFIRE OF LEAVES

Down, down came the leaves.

Down came the red leaves. Down came the yellow leaves. Down came the brown leaves.

They made big piles under the trees. They made big piles beside the fence. They made big piles around the two little white houses.

Martin and Judy had fun with the leaves. They ran through the leaves. They jumped into the leaves. They tossed the leaves into the air.

"Well," said Judy's father one day, "I think we will take out the rakes this morning."

Judy was glad that they were going to rake leaves. She ran to tell Martin all about it.

Judy and Martin liked to rake leaves. They liked to watch Judy's father burn leaves. They liked to smell the bonfire smoke.

Judy's father had a big rake.

Judy's brother and Martin's sister had middle-sized rakes.

Judy and Martin had little rakes.

They all worked together raking leaves.

They raked the leaves into a great big pile beside the garage.

They kept on raking until there were no more leaves under the trees or beside the fence. They kept on raking until there were no more leaves around the two little white houses.

"Are you going to burn the leaves now, Daddy?" asked Judy. "Can we have a nice bonfire right now?"

"I don't know," said Judy's father. "I'll have to telephone the man at the fire station. He will tell us whether we may have a bonfire today."

Judy and Martin were surprised. They knew that children had to say, "Please, may I do this? Please, may I do that?"

They did not know that daddies ever had to say, "Please, may we do this? Please, may we do that?"

Judy and Martin went into the house with Judy's father. They waited while he talked with the man at the fire station.

When he had finished telephoning, Judy's father looked at Judy and Martin. He said, "No bonfire today. The man at the fire station says that everything is very dry and the wind is blowing. Sparks from the burning leaves might be blown away. They might set something else on fire. The man at the fire station is not going to let anyone have bonfires until after it rains."

Judy and Martin and Judy's father were sorry not to have the bonfire. They went out again to the yard.

Judy's father put away his big rake.

Judy's brother and Martin's sister put away their middle-sized rakes.

Judy and Martin put away their little rakes.

They all helped to put a big cover over the pile of leaves.

"Now the leaves won't blow away or get wet," said Judy's father. "As soon as the man at the fire station will let us, we will have a bonfire."

Days and days and days went by.

Then came the day when it rained.

Judy and Martin were glad for the rain. They were glad when the man at the fire station said, "Now you may have your bonfire if you are careful."

Judy and Martin liked to watch the leaves burning.

They liked to hear the fire crackling.

They liked to smell the bonfire smoking.

"Bonfires are fun," said Martin and Judy.

HOP! JUMP! RUN!

Hop, jump, run!
Judy was playing with her shadow.
She hopped and her shadow hopped before her.
She jumped and her shadow jumped before her.
She ran and her shadow ran before her.
Judy sang a little song:

"Shadow and I go hop, jump, run.
Shadow and I go hop, jump, run.
Shadow and I, shadow and I
Like to play together."

Martin was in the next yard. He heard Judy singing. He came over to look through the fence.

"What are you doing, Judy?" asked Martin.

"I'm playing with my shadow," said Judy.

Martin climbed over the fence.

"Let me play with your shadow, too," said Martin.

Martin jumped on Judy's shadow.

"Don't jump on my shadow," said Judy. "Play with your own shadow."

Martin looked surprised. "I haven't any shadow," said Martin.

Judy looked in front of Martin.

She looked behind Martin.

"Oh," said Judy. "Turn around, Martin. Turn around fast. Your shadow is behind you."

Martin turned around fast. There, sure enough, was his very own shadow.

So Martin went hop, jump, run, playing with his shadow.

"My shadow is bigger than yours," called Martin. "My shadow is bigger than yours."

"I don't care if it is," called Judy. "I don't care if it is."

Martin and Judy went hop, jump, run.

Martin and Judy ran after their shadows.

But they never could catch up with them.

Always the shadows were running ahead.

Then Martin and Judy turned right around.

They ran in front of their shadows.

But they never could run away from them.

Always the shadows were close behind.

"We can't run away from our shadows," said Martin.

"We can't catch up with them, either," said Judy.

"Let's find something we can catch," said Martin. "Let's find it right away."

Martin and Judy found their two big rubber balls.

They rolled the balls across the yard.

Martin and Judy ran after them.

The two big rubber balls did not keep rolling ahead.

They rolled slower and slower until they stopped.

Martin and Judy could pick them up.

They could throw them and bounce them and roll them.

After a while Judy's mother came out on the porch.

"It's time for dinner now," said Judy's mother. "Martin may eat with us today. His mother said he might do so."

"Let's run," shouted Judy.

"Here I come," shouted Martin.

"Oh," sang Judy, "here's my shadow running before me."

"Oh," sang Martin, "here's my shadow running before me."

Martin and Judy had forgotten their shadows. They were surprised when they looked at them.

"My shadow isn't long any more," said Martin.

"My shadow is a baby shadow now," said Judy.

"What's the matter with our shadows?" asked Martin and Judy together.

Judy's mother looked at Judy's shadow. She looked at Martin's shadow. They were both very small.

"It is noontime now," said Judy's mother. "The sun is shining down from right over your heads. That's why your shadows are small."

"Will they grow big again?" asked Judy.

"Yes," said Judy's mother. "Your shadows will grow big again. Look for them this afternoon after your rest."

So Judy and Martin went into Judy's little white house.

They ate their lunches.

They lay down for their naps.

When rest time was over, they ran out to play in the yard.

Then they remembered to look for their shadows.

"See! Judy, see! My shadow is big again."

"So is mine, Martin. My shadow is big again, too."

Martin and Judy went hop, jump, run.

They hopped and their shadows hopped before them.

They jumped and their shadows jumped before them.

They ran and their shadows ran before them.

They sang their little song:

> "Shadow and I go hop, jump, run.
> Shadow and I go hop, jump, run.
> Shadow and I, shadow and I
> Like to play together."

SHADOWS AGAIN

THE sun was shining brightly.

It was shining on the little white house where Judy lived.

It was shining on the little white house where Martin lived.

It was shining on Judy and Martin, playing in Judy's yard.

"Look, Judy," said Martin. "There's a shadow girl beside you."

"Yes, Martin," said Judy. "There's a shadow boy beside you, too."

Everywhere that Judy and Martin went, the shadow girl and shadow boy went, too.

Everything that Judy and Martin did, the shadow girl and shadow boy did, too.

Judy and Martin ran around the little white house where Judy lived.

Judy and Martin saw a big black shadow. It looked like a big black house.

Judy and Martin walked around the big black shadow house.

They walked on top of the big black shadow house.

"Now we're walking on the roof," said Martin.

Judy and Martin put their hands on the tall black shadow chimney.

"Now we're touching the chimney," said Judy.

"But I can't feel the chimney," said Martin. "I can just feel the grass."

Then Judy and Martin knew it was just a shadow house that they were standing on.

Judy and Martin walked over to a tall maple tree.

They saw a big tall shadow beside it.

"Now I'm walking up the side of the tree," said Martin.

"Here I am, standing right on top of the tree," said Judy.

Everywhere that Judy and Martin went, the shadow girl and shadow boy went, too.

Judy and Martin found Judy's mother, hanging clothes on the line.

"Look, Mother, look," said Judy. "There's a shadow mother beside you."

They found Dusky, the cat, stretching herself in the sunshine.

"Look, Judy, look," said Martin. "There's a shadow cat beside Dusky, too."

"Have you been having fun?" asked Judy's mother.

"Oh, yes, we've been walking on the roof!" said Martin. "We've been touching the chimney!"

"We've been walking up the tree!" said Judy. "We've been standing on top of the tree!"

Judy's mother looked very much surprised.

"Will you show me?" asked Judy's mother.

Everywhere that Judy and Martin went, the shadow girl and shadow boy went, too.

Everywhere that Judy's mother went, the shadow mother went, too.

Everywhere that Dusky went, the shadow cat went, too.

Judy and Martin walked on top of the big black shadow house. They put their hands on the big black shadow chimney.

"Now we're walking on the roof," said Martin. "Now we're touching the chimney."

"I see! I see!" said Judy's mother.

Judy and Martin walked up to the top of the shadow tree.

"Now we're walking up the tree," said Judy. "We're standing right on top of the tree."

"I see! I see!" said Judy's mother.

Just then the sun stopped shining brightly.

The shadow house went away.

The shadow tree went away.

The shadow mother went away.

The shadow girl and shadow boy went away.

The shadow cat went away.

The real house and tree were still there. The real mother and girl and boy and cat were still there, too.

Judy's mother looked up at the sky.

"Do you know where you're standing now?" asked Judy's mother.

"No, we don't. Where are we?" said Judy and Martin.

"Now you're standing on a shadow cloud," said Judy's mother. "Shadow clouds are the biggest shadows of all."

Judy and Martin looked up.

They saw a big dark cloud, hiding the sun. It was far, far up in the sky above them.

Judy and Martin looked down at the ground.

"Now we're standing on a shadow cloud," sang Judy.

"Shadow clouds are the biggest shadows of all," sang Martin.

Judy's mother went away into the house.

Judy and Martin played on the shadow cloud until it went away. The sun shone brightly again.

The shadow girl and the shadow boy came back again.

The real girl and the real boy were very glad.

MARTIN GOES VISITING

MARTIN walked down the driveway. He walked over into Judy's yard. He could not find Judy anywhere.

Martin looked up the street. He looked down the street. He could not see anyone to play with.

Martin walked back into the house.

Martin's big sister was reading.

She said, "What do you want, Martin?"

Martin said, "Will you come and play with me?"

"I'm sorry, I can't play now," said Martin's big sister. "I am going to a meeting this afternoon."

Martin's mother was sewing.

She said, "What do you want, Martin?"

Martin said, "Will you come and play with me?"

"I'm sorry, I can't play now," said Martin's mother. "I am going to have company this afternoon."

Martin sat down. He felt very much alone. He could not think what to do.

"Oh, dear," said Martin to his mother. "I haven't anyone to play with. Everybody has something else to do."

"Make yourself a surprise," said Mother. "Think hard. Perhaps there is someone who'd like a little boy to play with.

"She may not be in our house.

"She may not be in Judy's house.

"But she must be in somebody's house."

Martin thought and thought.

He thought of the boys he knew.

He thought of the girls he knew.

He thought of the men and women he knew.

At last he thought of old Mrs. Dana.

Mrs. Dana lived in a house all by herself.

Mrs. Dana might be wishing for someone to visit with.

"May I go to Mrs. Dana's house?" asked Martin.

"Indeed you may," said Mother.

Martin jumped up. "I will go right now," said Martin.

"Would you like to take a jar of jelly for old Mrs. Dana?" asked Martin's mother.

"Oh, yes," said Martin. "I will take my puzzles to play with, too."

Away walked Martin down the sidewalk to old Mrs. Dana's house.

In one hand he carried a jar of jelly. In the other hand he carried his puzzles to play with Mrs. Dana.

Up the walk went Martin to old Mrs. Dana's door.

Martin wondered whether old Mrs. Dana was at home. He wondered whether she was busy.

He put his jar of jelly down on the step. He put his puzzles down beside the jelly. He put his hand up to knock on the door.

Tap, tap went Martin's hand on the outside of the door.

Step, step went someone's feet on the floor behind the door.

Squeak, squeak went the hinges at the side of the door.

Martin looked up. The door swung open.

There stood old Mrs. Dana, smiling down at Martin.

She looked very glad.

"Why, Martin," said Mrs. Dana. "I'm so glad you came. I was just wishing for someone to visit with."

"So was I," said Martin.

"I brought you some jelly, Mrs. Dana."

"Thank you very much," said old Mrs. Dana.

She put the jelly away in her cupboard.

"Would you like to play puzzles with me?" asked Martin.

"I'd love to," said old Mrs. Dana.

Martin and old Mrs. Dana played with puzzles for a long time.

Martin and old Mrs. Dana had a good time playing with puzzles.

Martin's mother had a good time with her company.
Martin's big sister had a good time at her meeting.
Everyone had something to do.

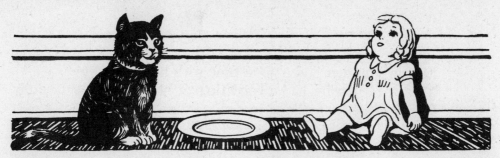

SARAH, THE DOLL, AND DUSKY, THE CAT

"WE are going to Grandmother's for a visit," said Judy's mother. "We must think what we want to take with us."

Judy sat down to think what she would take, when they went on a visit to Grandmother's.

"I will take my red dress," said Judy. "And my red hair-ribbon."

"Yes," said Mother.

"I will take my crayons," said Judy. "And my drawing-book."

"Yes," said Mother.

"I will take my doll, Sarah," said Judy. "And my cat, Dusky."

"We won't have room to take too many things," said Mother. "There will be books and magazines to take to Grandmother and Grandfather. There will be apples and potatoes to bring home from Grandmother's farm.

"Oh," said Judy.

"Would you rather take your doll, Sarah, or your cat, Dusky?" asked Mother.

Judy sat still to think about that, too.

She asked, "If we left Dusky, the cat, at home, who would give Dusky her dinner?"

"I don't know," said Mother. "If we left Sarah, the doll, at home, who would give Sarah her dinner?"

"Well," said Judy, "Sarah, the doll, only makes-believe eat. She would be all right without any dinner. But who would let Dusky, the cat, out in the morning? Who would let her in at night?"

"I don't know," said Mother. "Who would put Sarah, the doll, to bed at night? Who would dress her in the morning?"

"Oh," said Judy, "Sarah, the doll, just makes-believe sleep. It wouldn't hurt her to sit up all night."

"I see," said Mother. "Then what do you think we had better do?"

"We will take Dusky, the cat," said Judy. "We will leave Sarah, the doll, at home. Dusky, the cat, has to eat and sleep. She is alive. We must take care of her."

So Dusky, the cat, went to Grandmother's for a visit.

Sarah, the doll, stayed at home.

For Sarah, the doll, could not eat or sleep.

Sarah, the doll, was not alive.

She could be left alone.

But Dusky, the cat, could both eat and sleep.

Dusky, the cat, was alive.

She needed someone to care for her.

TO GRANDFATHER'S FARM

ROUND and round went the wheels of the car — round and round and round.

Judy and her family were all in the car.

Judy's father was driving the car. Judy's mother was holding the baby. Judy and her big brother were sitting on the back seat, with a basket between them. Dusky, the cat, was asleep in the basket.

Judy and her family were riding to Grandfather's farm.

They were wishing to be there soon.

Baby Sister did not remember the farm at all.

Baby Sister was only one year old.

But Judy remembered having fun at the farm before.

Judy wanted to see Grandfather.

Judy wanted to see Grandmother.

She wanted to see all the animals, and especially the baby calf.

Round and round went the wheels of the car — round and round and round.

"How many miles do we have to go now?" asked Judy.

"Four miles," answered Judy's father.

"Will it take long?" asked Judy.

"Not long at all," said Judy's father.

"Oh," said Judy. "Soon we'll see the baby calf! Do you remember, Mother? The baby calf with the wobbly legs?"

"Yes, I remember the baby calf," said Mother. "Her name was Jenny."

Round and round went the wheels of the car — round and round and round.

"Three miles now," said Judy's father.

Round and round went the wheels of the car — round and round and round.

"Two miles now," said Judy's father.

Round and round went the wheels of the car — round and round and round.

"One mile now," said Judy's father.

"I can see Grandfather's house," said Judy's big brother.

"I can see the barn where Jenny lives," said Judy.

Round and round went the wheels of the car — round and round and round.

They went right up the drive beside Grandfather's house.

"Here we are," said Judy's father.

Everybody was happy.

They all sat down on the porch together.

Baby Sister sat on Grandmother's lap.

Judy sat on Grandfather's knee.

"I want to see the baby calf," said Judy.

"So you do, so you do," said Grandfather. "Let's go out to the barn."

Judy and Grandfather hurried out together.

Judy looked all around the barn. She looked and looked again.

"Where is the baby calf, Grandfather?" asked Judy.

"It's right there," said Grandfather, "right there in front of you."

Judy looked and looked all around. "But, Grandfather, I mean the baby calf, the one with the wobbly legs. I mean Jenny."

"Sure enough," said Grandfather. "You're seeing Jenny right there. She's a big calf now. Her wobbly legs have grown strong. Jenny is one year old, you know."

Judy thought and thought about it. She could hardly believe that Jenny was so big.

"Baby Sister is one year old," said Judy. "Baby Sister is not so big."

"But a calf can grow very fast," said Grandfather. "Baby Sister grows more slowly. Next summer, when you come again, Jenny will be all grown up. She will be a cow."

Judy was surprised. "Oh," she said. "I'm four years old. I'm not as big as I'll be some day. Am I, Grandfather?"

"Some day, Judy, you'll probably be as big as your mother," said Grandfather.

"Next summer will I be as big as my mother?" asked Judy.

"No, not next summer. Not for a great many summers, Judy."

"Jenny grows fast," said Judy. "I grow slowly. How can calves grow so fast, Grandfather?"

"I don't know," said Grandfather. "Nobody knows. Some things grow fast. Some things grow slowly."

"Sarah, the doll, never grows at all," said Judy. "She is not alive. But babies and calves are alive. I am alive. Baby Sister and Jenny and I can grow and grow and grow."

BABY SISTER'S CHRISTMAS GIFT

THE sun shone on the little white house where Judy lived.

It was just two days before Christmas. It was the time of the giving of gifts.

"Christmas is coming soon," sang Judy. "Christmas is coming soon."

"Ooly-ooly-oo," sang Judy's baby sister. "Ooly-ooly-oo."

Judy's baby sister did not know about Christmas. She had not heard Christmas singing. She had not seen a Christmas tree. She had been only a few weeks old at Christmas time last year. She could not know about it.

Judy tried to tell her baby sister about Christmas.

"Christmas is coming soon," said Judy. "Christmas is coming day after tomorrow."

Baby Sister looked at Judy. She seemed to be listening to what Judy was saying.

Judy knew about Christmas. She knew it was the birthday of Jesus.

Judy had never seen Jesus. Jesus had lived before Judy was born.

Judy liked Jesus' birthday. Jesus' birthday seemed like everybody's birthday. It was the time of the giving of gifts.

Judy had had fun making Christmas gifts for people she loved.

She had made her mother a tea-pot stand. Judy's big brother had helped her make it of clay. Judy painted it with some bright blue paint her brother had given her.

Judy had made her daddy an ash-tray of clay. She painted the tray with bright red paint her brother had given her.

She had made Big Brother a calendar to keep on his desk. Judy had done this all by herself.

She had made Dusky, the cat, a warm little blanket to lie on. Mother had found the cloth and Judy had cut it out.

Now she was wondering what she could give her baby sister.

"What can I put on the Christmas tree for Baby Sister?" asked Judy.

"What do you think she would like?" asked Judy's mother.

Judy thought of the things she liked. Perhaps Baby Sister would like them, too. She thought of candy and scissors and a doll and a book.

"I can't give Baby Sister candy," said Judy. "Candy isn't good for her."

"No," said Mother, "candy wouldn't do."

"I can't give her scissors," said Judy. "She would cut herself with scissors."

"No," said Mother, "scissors wouldn't do at all."

"I don't want to give her a doll," said Judy. "She has a doll already."

"No," said Mother, "she doesn't need another doll."

"I don't want to give her a book," said Judy. "She tears books."

"No," said Mother. "She is not quite old enough for books."

"Oh, dear," said Judy. "What can I put on the Christmas tree for Baby Sister?"

"I have a thought," said Judy's mother. "Baby Sister has no toys to play with in the tub when she takes her bath."

"Oh, yes," said Judy. "Baby Sister would like a duck to swim in the bath-tub. I will buy her a duck for Christmas."

That afternoon Judy went with her big brother to the store. She bought a toy duck for Baby Sister. It was just the right kind to swim in the bath-tub, when Baby Sister was having her bath. Judy took the duck home and put it with the other gifts which she was going to give.

"Christmas is coming soon," sang Judy. "Christmas is coming day after tomorrow."

"Ooly-ooly-oo," sang Judy's baby sister. "Ooly-ooly-oo."

[58]

Judy was very happy. She was thinking about Christmas — the birthday of Jesus — the time of the giving of gifts.

Judy's baby sister did not know about Christmas, but she was very happy, too.

SURPRISE! SURPRISE!

THE sun shone on the two little white houses where Martin and Judy lived.

It was the day before Christmas. It was the day before Jesus' birthday. It was the time of the giving of gifts.

In one little white house, Martin and his mother were wrapping Christmas gifts. Martin was wrapping his gift for Judy.

Martin's gift for Judy was a box of paints.

"Judy will like these paints," said Martin. "She likes to use my paints when she plays with me."

Martin wrapped the box of paints in white paper. He tied it with red ribbon. Martin's mother helped him to fold the paper straight and to tie the ribbon bow.

In the other little white house, Judy and her mother were wrapping Christmas gifts, too. Judy was wrapping her gift for Martin.

Judy's gift for Martin was a bright red rubber ball.

"Martin needs a new ball," said Judy. "Stubby, the dog, chewed the old ball. It will not bounce any more."

Judy wrapped the ball in pretty green paper. She tied it with silver ribbon. Judy's mother helped her to fold the paper and to tie the ribbon bow.

When Judy had finished wrapping her gift for Martin, she went to the window. She saw Martin just going out the *back* door of his little white house.

"Oh, look," said Judy. "Martin is going out into his yard. If I take his gift over now, Martin will see me. I don't want Martin to see me. I want it to be a surprise."

"You could go to the *front* door," said Judy's mother. "I don't think Martin would see you then."

Judy hurried into her outdoor clothes. She went out the *front* door of her little white house. She hurried along the sidewalk toward Martin's little white house. She thought that Martin did not see her.

Up the path walked Judy, to the *front* door of Martin's little white house. Zmmmm, zmmmm went the doorbell.

In a few minutes Martin's mother came to the door. She smiled at Judy.

Judy held out Martin's Christmas gift, in its green paper and silver ribbon.

"This is for Martin," said Judy. "It is a surprise."

"Thank you very much, Judy," said Martin's mother. "I'll put it on the Christmas tree for Martin."

Judy walked down the front steps of Martin's little white house. She thought that Martin had not seen her at all.

But Martin had seen Judy. He did not know where Judy was going. He did not know that she was carrying a Christmas gift for him.

Martin thought to himself, "Judy is going away. Now I can take her gift to her house, and Judy will not see me. Then it will be a surprise."

Martin ran to get his gift for Judy. He ran across the yard. He climbed over the fence.

Up the path ran Martin, to the *back* door of Judy's little white house. Judy's mother opened the door and smiled at Martin.

Martin held out Judy's Christmas gift, in its white paper and red ribbon.

"Here is a surprise for Judy," said Martin.

"Oh, thank you, Martin," said Judy's mother. "I'll put it on the Christmas tree for her."

Martin ran back to his own yard.

Judy walked back to her own front door.

Martin did not know where Judy had been.

Judy did not know what Martin had been doing.

The next morning was Christmas. It was the birthday of Jesus. It was the time of giving gifts.

In one little white house, Judy's family were sitting around their Christmas tree. It was a big tree with bright shining trimmings.

Judy's family were having fun opening the gifts that they found under the tree.

They liked to *give* gifts to the ones they loved.

They liked to *receive* gifts from the ones they loved.

In the other little white house, Martin's family were sitting around their Christmas tree. It was a little tree with bright shining trimmings.

Martin's family were having fun opening the gifts that they found under the tree.

They liked to *give* gifts to those they loved.

They liked to *receive* gifts from those they loved.

In the afternoon Martin and Judy played together in Judy's house.

They made bright pictures with Judy's new paints.

"Christmas is like everybody's birthday," said Martin. "Your birthday and my birthday! Everybody's birthday!"

Martin and Judy laughed.

They painted more pictures with Judy's new paints.

Then Judy and Martin put on their coats and went out of doors.

They played a long time with Martin's red ball.

Martin and Judy were glad to have Christmas come.

Everybody in the two little white houses was glad to have Christmas come.

For Christmas *was* like everybody's birthday.

HIDING IN THE DARK

EVERY night the darkness came to Martin's house. It came to Judy's house.

It came to all the other houses in the town. It came to all the other towns and cities.

Every night after the darkness came, Judy and her mother went up to the bathroom together.

Judy took off her day clothes.

She had a bath in the big tub.

She put on her night clothes. She put on her bathrobe and slippers.

She went downstairs to have her supper.

Every night after supper, Judy and her mother went up to Judy's room.

They turned on the light. They looked all around to see that everything was in its place. They turned the light off again.

Then Judy and her mother went out into the hall.

"It's your turn first tonight, Mother," said Judy.

Judy's mother went into Judy's room. She went out of sight in the darkness. Judy could not see her at all.

After a little while Judy heard Mother's voice.

> "Judy, Judy,
> The dark is hiding me.
> Tell me where I am."

Judy tried to tell where Mother's voice came from.

She said, "I guess you are standing beside my table."

"No," said Mother. "I am not standing beside your table."

"Judy, Judy,
    The dark is hiding me.
    Tell me where I am."

Judy tried again to tell where Mother's voice came from.
She said, "I guess you are standing beside my chair."
"Yes," said Mother, "I am standing beside your chair."
"Now you must come out," said Judy. She waited until her mother came out into the hall.
Judy said, "It is my turn now."
Judy went into her room. She went into the darkness. She knew that her mother could not see her at all.
Judy crawled under her bed. She said.

"Mother, Mother,
    The dark is hiding me.
    Tell me where I am."

Judy's mother tried to tell where Judy's voice came from.
She said, "I guess you are sitting in your chair."
"No," said Judy, "I am not sitting in my chair."

"Mother, Mother,
    The dark is hiding me.
    Tell me where I am."

Judy's mother tried again to tell where Judy's voice came from.
She said, "I guess you are under your bed."
"Yes," said Judy, "I am under my bed."
"Oho," said Mother. "Now you must hop right into your bed. We shall play our game again tomorrow night."
Judy took off her bathrobe and hung it on her chair.
She took off her slippers and put them under her chair.
She hopped into her bed and pulled up the blankets.
Judy's mother opened the window.
She kissed Judy good night.
She went out and closed the door.

Judy lay still with the darkness all around her. She thought of the game which she and Mother had played.

Sometimes Judy kept on playing a game.

Sometimes she said:

> "Table, table,
> The dark is hiding you,
> But I know where you are."

Sometimes she said:

> "Chair, chair,
> The dark is hiding you,
> But I know where you are."

Sometimes she said:

> "Window, window,
> The dark is hiding you,
> But I know where you are."

Sometimes Judy went to sleep in the middle of her game.

Then the darkness kept right on hiding Judy.

The darkness kept right on hiding the table and the chair and the window.

The darkness kept right on hiding all the things in Judy's room, until the daylight came again and found them.

MARTIN'S FUN WITH DREAMING

IT was nighttime in the little white house where Martin lived.
It was very dark.

Martin was lying in his bed, with the darkness all around him.

Now and then an automobile went by the house where Martin lived.

Martin did not hear the automobile.

Now and then a light shone into Martin's window.

Martin did not see the light.

Once Martin's mother came into his room to see that he was covered warmly.

Martin did not know that his mother came in.

Martin was asleep.

He lay in his bed, with the darkness all around him.

He did not know that he was asleep.

Martin was having a dream. In his dream, Martin was not lying in his bed, with darkness all around him.

In his dream Martin was doing other things.

He was running very fast around his yard. He was running so fast that Stubby could not catch him.

Stubby could always catch Martin, when they played together in the yard.

Stubby could not catch Martin, in Martin's dream. Martin had fun, running away from Stubby.

In his dream Martin was doing still other things.

He was climbing the big tree in his yard. He was climbing so high that he could see over the house.

The big tree in Martin's yard was very tall. It was too tall for Martin to climb.

In his dream the big tree was not too tall. Martin had fun, climbing the tall tree.

In his dream Martin was doing still other things.

He was doing things he never could do when he was awake.

Martin had fun doing the things he had never been able to do.

Then Martin woke up. He knew that he had been dreaming.

He knew that he was lying in his bed, with the morning light making a path across his floor.

Martin knew that he had not really run too fast for Stubby to catch him.

He knew that he had not really climbed the tall tree and looked over the house.

He knew that he had had a dream that was fun.

Martin was a little sorry to know that it was just a dream.

He hurried away to tell Mother all about it.

"Mother," said Martin. "Mother, I had a dream. It was a nice dream, too."

"Tell me about it, Martin," said Mother.

"In my dream," said Martin, "I was running so fast that Stubby couldn't catch me."

"Good for you," said Mother. "That must have been fun."

"Yes," said Martin. "And in my dream I climbed the big tree in the yard. I climbed way up until I could see over the house."

"That must have been fun, too," said Mother.

"In my dream I did lots of things," said Martin. "And then I woke up, and I was right in my bed! I'd been right in my bed all the time."

"I'm glad you had a nice dream," said Martin's mother.

"I hope I'll have another dream just like that one," said Martin.

"Perhaps you will," said Martin's mother. "But dreams are like surprises. We can't tell when they're coming, or what they're going to be."

MARTIN'S OTHER DREAM

MARTIN was all ready to hop into bed.

Martin's mother was all ready to tuck him in and say good night.

Martin looked at his bed. It made him think of something.

"Mother," said Martin, "I had a dream last night, didn't I?"

"Yes," said Martin's mother. "You had a dream that was fun."

Martin hopped into bed as fast as he could. "I hope I'll have another dream," said Martin.

All night long Martin lay in his bed with the darkness all around him.

He did not hear the automobiles going by.

He did not see the lights shining in through his window.

He did not know when his mother came in to see that he was covered warmly.

Martin was asleep.

Martin did not dream that he was running too fast for Stubby to catch him.

He did not dream that he was climbing the tall tree in the yard.

He did not dream anything at all.

For one, two, three nights Martin did not have any dreams.

He almost forgot that he had ever had a dream.

On the fourth night Martin was lying in his bed with the darkness all around him.

He did not hear the automobiles going by.

He did not see the lights shining in through his window.

He did not know when his mother came in to see that he was covered warmly.

Martin was asleep. He was having another dream.

He hurried downstairs to tell his mother all about it.

"In my dream," said Martin, "I couldn't do anything I tried to do."

"Yes," said his mother. "I have had dreams like that, too."

"I hope I won't have another dream like that," said Martin.

"Almost everybody has a bad dream once in a while," said Mother. "Do you know there is often something nice, even about bad dreams?"

"No, what?" asked Martin.

"Well, in this dream, Martin, you were trying very hard to do something all by yourself. That's a good thing."

"But, I don't have to try hard to go upstairs," said Martin. "I can climb them fast."

Mother laughed a little. "Dream stairs are not like real stairs, Martin."

"I know," said Martin. "I just made up the dream stairs in my sleep, didn't I?"

"That's it," said Mother.

"Well, I like nice dreams." Martin was quiet for a minute. He was thinking. "And I had to go and make up a bad one. Why did I, Mother?"

"Because," said Mother, "you didn't feel like a nice dream last night. We dream the way we feel."

"And nobody knows what I'm dreaming till I wake up and tell them, do they, Mother?"

"Nobody," said Mother. "I'm glad, though, that you tell me your bad dreams and your good ones, too."

Martin did not answer. He thought of something all of a sudden. He ran across the room. He hurried all the way up to the top of the stairs and shouted down to his mother.

"See! I did it. I'm at the top, and it was easy as could be."

"I hope I won't have another dream like that," said Martin.

"I hope you won't," said Mother. "But do you know something nice, even about bad dreams?"

"No, what?" asked Martin.

"We always wake up," said Mother. "We always wake up and find that the dream wasn't real at all!"

NIGHTTIME

IT was very dark in the two little white houses.

It was nighttime.

Martin and his father and his mother and his big sister were all fast asleep in their beds.

Judy and her father and her mother, too, were all fast asleep in their beds. So were Judy's big brother and her baby sister.

There was no one walking on the sidewalk in front of the little white houses.

There were no cars going along the street.

Only the dark was there, covering everything, and the wind blowing down the street very fast.

The wind tossed the branches of the trees. It rattled the shutters of Judy's little white house.

Judy's window was open. The wind blew in, whistling "Ou-ou-ou, ou-ou-ou."

It blew the window-shade on Judy's window. It made the shade go tap, tap, tap against the window-pane. The noise made Judy wake up.

Tap, tap, tap went the window-shade again. Judy did not know what it was. She did not like hearing the tap, tap, tap.

"Mother!" called Judy. "Mother! Mother!"

"Ou-ou-ou, ou-ou-ou," cried the wind, louder than Judy could call.

Judy's mother could not hear Judy calling. She could not hear the wind whistling. Judy's mother was fast asleep in the next room.

Tap, tap, tap went the window-shade. "Ou-ou-ou, ou-ou-ou," cried the wind outside.

Judy lay very still. She did not like being there all alone. She wished her mother would come.

[77]

Tap, tap, tap came the sound again. It did not sound any nearer than before. It did not sound any louder than before.

Judy lay very still. She did not mind the noise so much now. She tried to think.

"This is my room. All the things in it are my things."

"I am not afraid of my table."

"I am not afraid of my chair."

"I am not afraid of my toys."

"I am not afraid of my clothes."

"I am not afraid of anything in my room."

Tap, tap, tap came the sound again.

It did not sound like a door opening.

It did not sound like a man walking.

It did not sound like a cat scratching.

What did it sound like?

Judy thought to herself, "I will make-believe that I can see all around me."

She made-believe that she could see her table by the window. She made-believe that she could see her clothes on the chair. She made-believe that she could see the shelves by the wall where her toys were lying.

She knew just where everything was.

Her toys were on the shelves. Her clothes were on the chair. Her table was near the window.

Now she could really see the window.

Now she could really see the shade moving.

Now she could really hear the tap, tap, tap.

Now she knew where the noise had come from. Judy had heard the window-shade make that same noise before.

Judy did not mind the noise any more.

She did not mind the dark any more.

She did not try to call her mother any more.

She turned over and went to sleep.

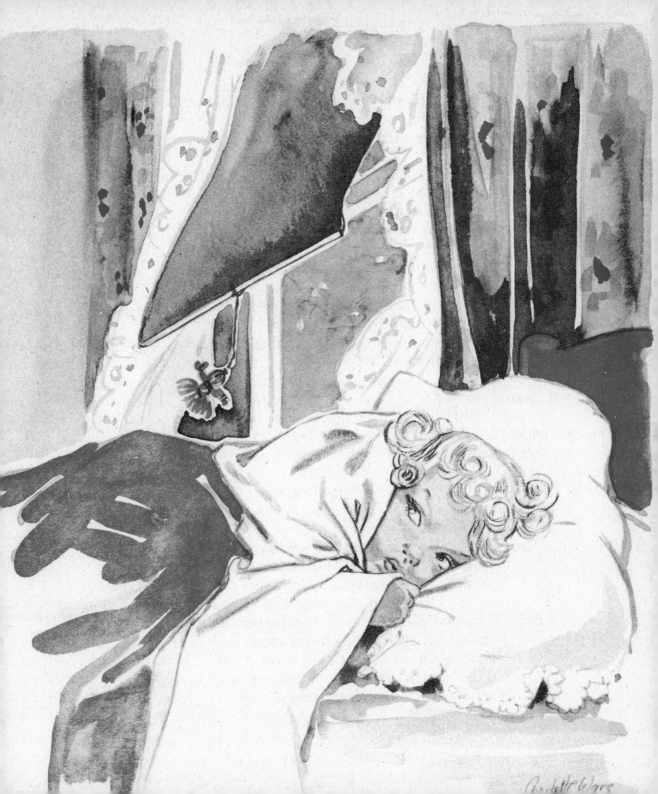

WHOSE HOUSE IS IT?

WHEN Judy awoke, just a little bit of daylight was shining through her windows.

Judy knew it was not time to get up. She lay still in her bed. Her eyes were wide open.

Judy looked up and down and around. She liked her room. She liked all the things that were in her room.

"This is my bed," sang Judy to herself.

"That is my chair.

"That is my table.

"Those are my shelves.

"Those are my clothes.

"Those are my toys.

"This is my room."

Judy lay still in her bed. She looked up and down and around. She liked her room. She liked all the things that were in her room.

"These are my windows," sang Judy to herself.

"These are my walls.

"This is my floor.

"This is my room.

"This is my house."

Judy's mother came into the room.

Judy knew it was now time to get up. She jumped out of bed. She danced about the room.

"Sing, song, this is my room," sang Judy as she danced.

"Sing, song, this is my house."

"Oh," said Mother. "This is your house, is it? Thank you for letting the rest of us live in it with you."

Judy's big brother came into the room.

"What is Judy saying, Mother?" asked Judy's big brother.

"I was saying, 'This is my house,'" said Judy.

Her big brother looked a little cross.

"It is not either your house. It's Daddy's house. It was his before you were born."

Daddy came into the room. Judy ran to him.

"Daddy, whose house is this?" she asked.

"Well, now, what would you say, Judy? Whose house do you think it is?"

Daddy smiled at Mother and at Judy. He smiled at Judy's big brother.

"I guess this house belongs to us all," said Judy. "But my room belongs to me, doesn't it, Daddy?"

"Yes, Judy," said Daddy. "Part of the house is yours.

"Part of the house is Mother's.

"Part of the house is Daddy's.

"Part of the house is Brother's.

"Part of the house is Baby Sister's.

"All of the house belongs to all of us."

Judy ran down the stairs. She ran out into the yard. She ran all around the house.

She looked at the front of the house.

She looked at the back of the house.

She looked at the sides of the house.

"Sing, song, this house belongs to us all," sang Judy as she ran.

"It is my mother's house.

"It is my father's house.

"It is my brother's house.

"It is our baby's house.

"It is Judy's house, too.

"Sing, song, this house belongs to us all."

Judy ran back into the house.

She sat in her chair at the table.

The family ate breakfast together.

Judy liked her family.
Judy liked their house.
Judy was very happy.

SNOW PICTURES

IT began to snow one night, just as Martin was going to bed.

"Oh, I hope it will snow all night long," said Martin to his mother. "I want the ground to be all white in the morning."

And it did snow all night long while Martin was fast asleep.

In the morning when Martin woke up, he looked out of his window.

He saw two shining white yards.

He saw snow on the fence and snow on the trees.

He saw snow on the garage roof, and snow on the roof of Judy's little white house.

When he was dressed, Martin ran downstairs. He looked out of one window. He looked out of another window.

He saw snow on the feeding-shelf where he put crumbs and seeds for the birds.

Things looked so different, with snow all around. Martin liked to look out on the shining white snow.

"We must be sure to feed the birds this morning," said Martin's mother. "They cannot find food for themselves, now that this snow has come."

Martin's mother opened the window. She gave Martin a little brush. Martin brushed the snow off the feeding-shelf.

He scattered crumbs and seeds around. Then they closed the window and stood looking out.

"Here comes a hungry birdie," said Martin.

"Oh," said Mother, "It's a chickadee!"

"He likes the sunflower seeds," said Martin. "See him hopping around to find them."

Hop, hop, hop went the chickadee among the seeds.

"Look, Mother, look," said Martin. "He hopped in the snow on the window-sill. He left a picture of his feet in the snow."

By and by other hungry birds came to look for food. Martin was putting on his snow suit. He and Stubby, the dog, were going out to play.

Out they went, into the shining white yard. It was snowing again. The flakes fell on Stubby's ears. They fell on Martin's snow suit. They were falling everywhere.

Step, step, step went Martin across the shining white yard to the fence.

Tippety, tippety, tippety went Stubby, the dog, ahead of him.

All the way across the yard they left their footprints, like pictures in the snow.

Martin looked back at the footprints.

"When I go home," said Martin to himself, "I can walk in the very same tracks."

He lifted Stubby over the fence into Judy's yard. Then Martin climbed over after him.

Judy and Martin had a great deal of fun.

They threw snowballs at the apple tree.

They rode down the drive on Judy's sled.

They built a big snow man.

Stubby, the dog, ran and ran — around and around.

Stubby liked the snow, too.

Down came the snowflakes, falling, falling through the air. They fell on Judy's snowsuit and hat and mittens. They fell on Martin's snow-suit and hat and mittens.

They were like little white pictures on the dark cloth.

At dinner-time Martin's mother called to him to come home.

"I'm going to walk back in the tracks that I made when I came over," said Martin.

He climbed up on the fence. He looked for his tracks in the snow.

Judy climbed up and looked for them, too.

The yard was just as smooth as it was before Martin had crossed it. The snowflakes, falling, falling, had covered all of Martin's footprints.

They had covered Stubby's footprints, too. They had even covered the chickadee's footprints on the window-sill.

"I'll have to make some new footprints," said Martin.

Step, step, step went Martin, leaving his footprints behind him, like pictures in the snow.

Down came the snowflakes, falling, falling, on the two little white houses, and the two shining white yards.